STAR WARS ®

Stories from a Galaxy
Far, Far Away....

LONDON, NEW YORK, MUNICH,
MELBOURNE, AND DELHI

Editor Kate Simkins
Project Editor Laura Gilbert
Senior Art Editor Nick Avery
Designers Jon Hall, Cathy Tincknell
Art Director Mark Richards
Publishing Manager Simon Beecroft
Category Publishers Alex Allan, Siobhan Williamson
Brand Manager Lisa Lanzarini
Production Rochelle Talary, Nick Seston
DTP Designers David McDonald, Lauren Egan, Santosh Kumar G

For Lucasfilm
Executive Editor Jonathan W. Rinzler
Art Editor Iain R. Morris
Art Director Troy Alders
Continuity Supervisor Leland Chee

Reading Consultant
Linda B. Gambrell, Professor and Director,
Eugene T. Moore School of Education, Clemson University.

This edition published in the United States in 2008.

First published in the United States in 2005 and 2007 as four separate titles:
Star Wars: What is a Wookie? 2005, *Star Wars: Ready, Set, Podrace!* 2007
Star Wars: Journey Through Space 2005 and *Star Wars: A Queen's Diary* 2007

Published in the United States by
DK Publishing, Inc., 375 Hudson Street, New York, New York 10014

08 09 10 11 12 10 9 8 7 6 5 4 3 2 1

Page design copyright © 2005, 2007 Dorling Kindersley Limited
Copyright © 2005, 2007 Lucasfilm Ltd. and ™.
All rights reserved. Used under authorization.

Published in Great Britain by Dorling Kindersley Limited.

A catalog record for this book is available from
the Library of Congress

ISBN 978-0-7566-5093-3

Color reproduction by Media Development and Printing, UK
Printed and bound in China by L. Rex Printing Co. Ltd.

Discover more at
www.dk.com
www.starwars.com

STAR WARS®

Stories from a Galaxy Far, Far Away....

Contents

STAR WARS™
What is a
Wookiee?

Written by Laura Buller and Kate Simkins

My name
is C-3PO.

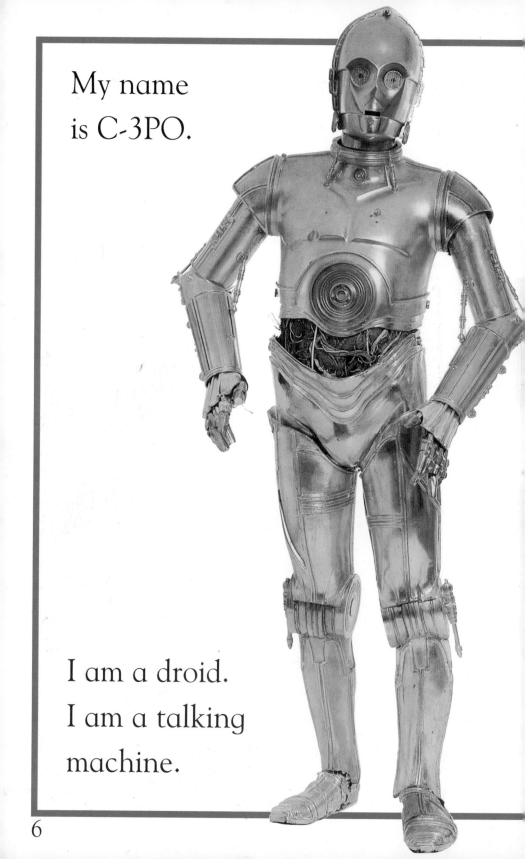

I am a droid.
I am a talking
machine.

I live far, far away in space.
Lots of creatures live here.
I will be telling you
about some of them.

Space

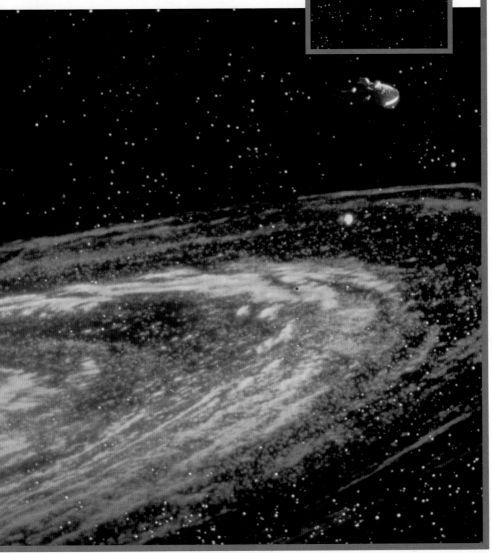

Some creatures in *Star Wars* are aliens.

Aliens are not human.
There are lots of different aliens.

Humans also live here—
my friend Padmé (PAD-MAY) is
a human.

This is my friend R2-D2.
He is a droid too.

R2-D2 likes talking.
His voice sounds like
whistles and beeps, but
I can understand him.

R2-D2 is a clever
little machine.
He has all sorts
of useful tools.
He can fix anything!

Tool

Meet Chewbacca.

He is a tall,
furry alien
called
a Wookiee.

He is the best friend of Han Solo,
who is a human.
They fly a spaceship together.

Sometimes,
I ride with them!

Spaceship

Now say hello
to Jar Jar Binks.

He is a friendly
alien.

Jar Jar comes from
an underwater city.
On land, Jar Jar is always
falling over!

He uses his long tongue
to catch food to eat.

Let's visit Watto's shop.

Watto is a blue alien.
He has a bad temper.
Watto flies about
using the wings on his back.

He sells bits of old machines
called junk.

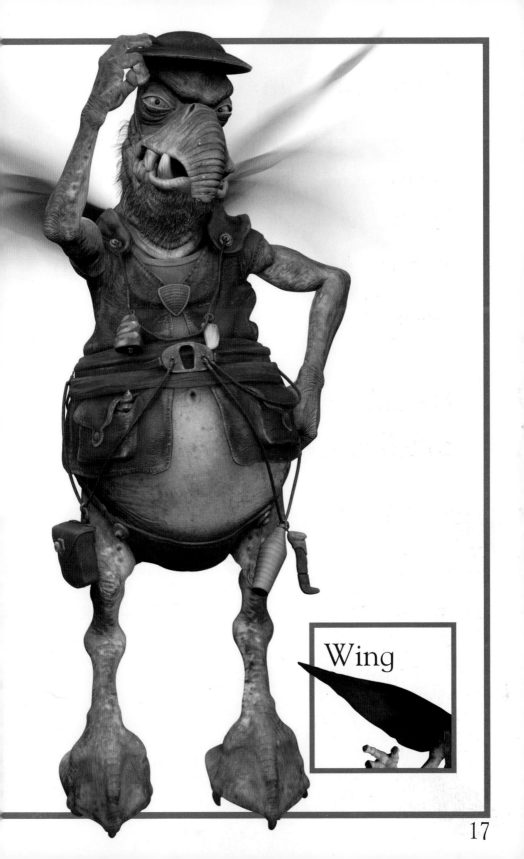

Wing

17

Now it's time
to meet Sebulba
(SEE-BUL-BAH).

This nasty alien
races in a vehicle
called a Podracer.
He likes to go fast.

Podracer

Sebulba will do anything to win.
He will even throw things
at other Podracers!

Pit droids fix the Podracers.
They are very useful and
can carry heavy things.

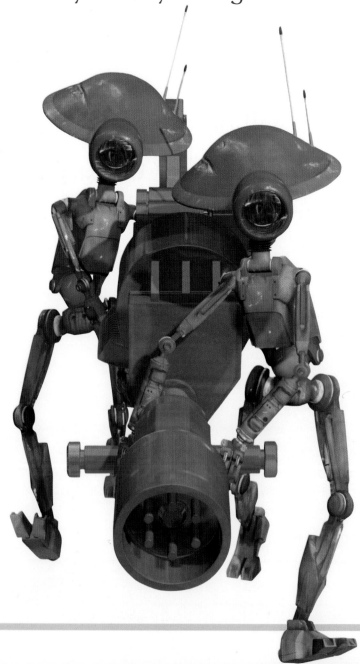

Pit droids sometimes
get into trouble.
There is one way to stop them.
Tap them on the nose
and they fold up.

Jabba the Hutt is a nasty alien.
He has a fat body and a long tail.
His body is covered in sticky slime.

Tail

Jabba's eyes are red and yellow and his breath is smelly. Don't get too near him!

Let's visit Dexter Jettster's
restaurant.

This friendly alien has four arms.
He cooks the food at Dexter's Diner.

Dexter knows lots of things.
What shall we ask him?

These creatures
are lizard keepers.

They live
in big holes
in the ground.

Sometimes, the lizard keepers ride around on giant lizards. The lizards are good at jumping and climbing.

Jawas are small creatures
with shiny yellow eyes.

Their faces
are hidden under
the hoods of
their brown cloaks.

Hood

These little aliens
find droids and
bits of machines to sell.

Once, they even sold
R2-D2!

If we go deep into the forest,
we may meet the Ewoks.

Ewoks are small, furry creatures.
They live in houses
that they build high up
in the trees.

Forest

Yoda is very old and very wise.
He has green skin and
big, pointy ears.

No one knows what kind
of creature he is or
where he comes from.

I hope you have enjoyed
learning about the creatures
in *Star Wars*.

Goodbye!

Picture word list

Space

page 7

Podracer

page 19

Tool

page 11

Tail

page 22

Spaceship

page 13

Hood

page 28

Wing

page 17

Forest

page 31

STAR WARS

READY, SET, PODRACE!

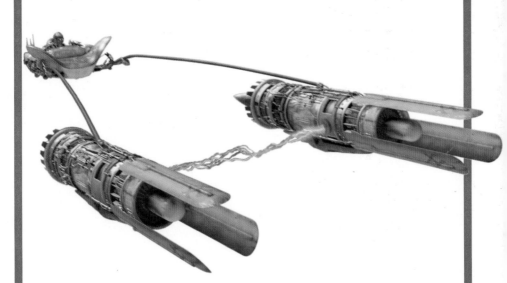

Written by Simon Beecroft

Do you like fast races?

Would you like to see
the fastest race ever?

A Podrace is the fastest race
you will ever see!

In a Podrace, each pilot flies
a machine called a Podracer.

Podracers fly just above
the ground.

Podracers fly very fast!

Podracer

Podracer pilots sit
in a seat called
a cockpit.

Cockpit

All the driving controls
are in front of them.

The pilots have to move
the controls very quickly
when they are racing.

Do you think you could fly
a Podracer?

This desert racetrack has lots of twists and turns.

Some of these twists and turns are very dangerous.

The pilot who
reaches the end
of the race first
is the winner.

Racetrack

Many people come to watch
the Podraces.
The people shout and cheer.

They are excited to see the race.
They want to find out
which racer will win.

Podracing is very dangerous.

The pilots fly along at really
fast speeds.

Some racers crash into each other, and some racers crash into cliffs.

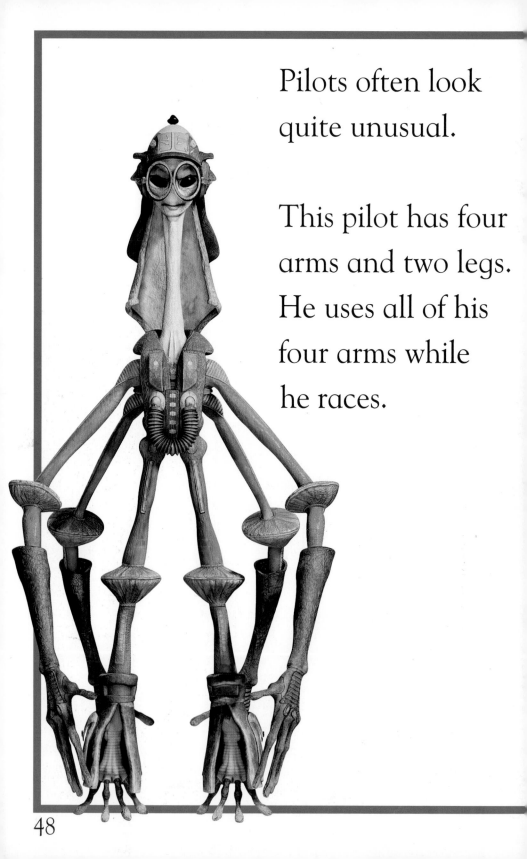

Pilots often look quite unusual.

This pilot has four arms and two legs. He uses all of his four arms while he races.

This pilot has three eyes.
His extra eye helps him
spot dangers in the race.

This pilot is wearing goggles.
They are special racing goggles.
His racing goggles
protect his eyes
from the desert sand.

This pilot is nervous.
He is worried because
his Podracer is broken.
He will not finish the race.

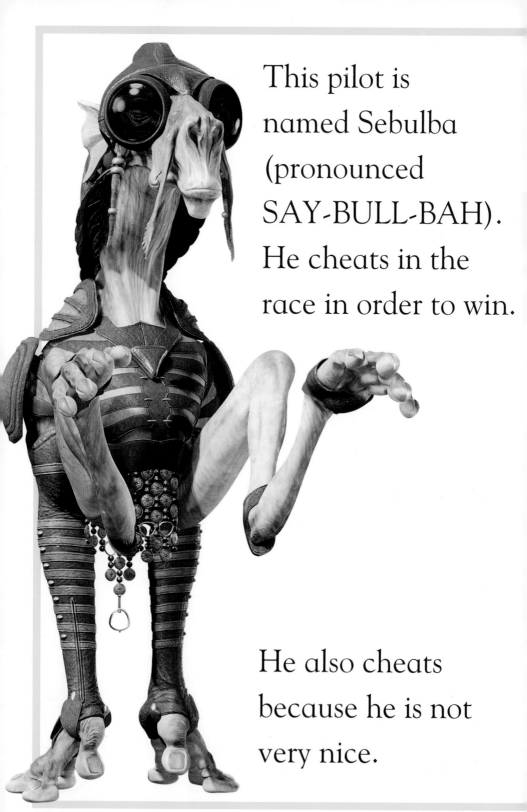

This pilot is named Sebulba (pronounced SAY-BULL-BAH). He cheats in the race in order to win.

He also cheats because he is not very nice.

Sebulba sometimes throws
his tools at the
other pilots.
He wants to
force them out
of the race.

Tools

Selbulba is a very
dangerous
racer.

Pilots prepare their machines
for the race in a big garage
called a hangar.

Robots clean
the Podracers and
repair the engines.

Each pilot makes
sure his Podracer
is ready to go!

Engines

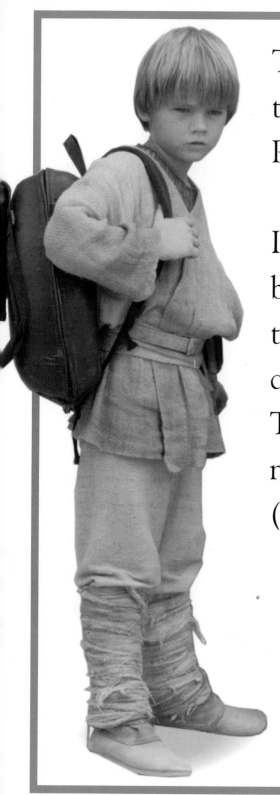

Today is one of the most exciting Podraces ever.

It is exciting because one of the racers is a young boy. The boy is named Anakin (AN-NA-KIN).

Anakin has never finished
a Podrace before.

Anakin built his Podracer all by himself.

He is only nine years old,
but he is a very good pilot.

Anakin's family and friends are
going to watch him race.

The pilots are on the starting line.
Ready, set,
Podrace!

The race is very exciting.
Sebulba does everything he can
to win.
He tries to push Anakin out
of the race.

Anakin is a better racer
than Sebulba.
Sebulba crashes!

Anakin wins the race.
Anakin's friends and family are
very happy, but Anakin is
happiest of all!

Glossary

Cockpit a space that a pilot sits in

Engines machines that make a vehicle move

Podracer a vehicle that flies close to the ground

Racetrack an oval piece of track that vehicles race on

Tools items that are used for mechanical work

STAR WARS™
Journey Through
SPACE

Written by Ryder Windham

Come on a journey through space
to the *Star Wars* galaxy.
It is far, far away.
In this galaxy, there are
many stars and planets.

Coruscant (CORE-RUS-SANT)
is the most important planet.
It is covered by one enormous city.
All the buildings in the city
are gleaming skyscrapers.

Jedi Knights

Many creatures live in
the *Star Wars* galaxy.
Coruscant is the home
of powerful warriors
called Jedi Knights.

Yoda

People and Gungans live on
the planet Naboo.
The people live in beautiful cities
on the land.
Young Padmé Amidala was once
Queen of Naboo.

*Queen
Amidala*

The Gungans live
in underwater cities.
They can walk
on land too,
although some are
a bit clumsy!
Jar Jar Binks
is a Gungan.

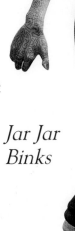

*Jar Jar
Binks*

Podracing

Tatooine is famous
for Podracing.
In this dangerous sport,
fast vehicles race each
other through the desert.

The planet Tatooine (TA-TOO-EEN)
is covered by a dusty desert.
Two suns shine in the sky so
it is very hot.
Tatooine is a meeting place.
Space travelers visit the planet from
all over the galaxy.

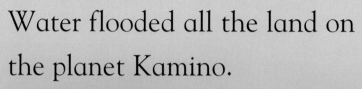

Water flooded all the land on
the planet Kamino.
So the Kaminoans built their cities
on strong metal poles that stick up
above the water.

Kaminoans are very tall with long, thin necks. They ride winged beasts to fly and swim around their watery planet.

Geonosis (GEE-OH-NO-SIS) is not a good place to be captured. Prisoners are forced to fight huge monsters in special arenas.

Huge arenas
The arenas are made of rock. There are lots of seats inside.

Scary beasts are brought from other
planets to the arenas.
The Geonosians look like insects
and enjoy watching the fights.

Chewbacca

Tarfful

Kashyyyk (KASH-ICK) is a world
of giant trees and shallow lakes.
It is home to the Wookiees,
including Chewbacca and Tarfful.
Wookiees are tall and have lots
of shaggy fur.
They talk in grunts and roars.

Good friends

Chewbacca is friends
with a human
called Han Solo.
They fly together
in a starship—the
Millennium Falcon.

The planet Utapau
(OO-TA-POW)
has lots of deep holes.
The Utapauns dig
tunnels through
the rocks to join
the holes.

There are other
creatures on
the planet.

An Utapaun

Creatures called
Utai (OO-TIE) live in
holes in the ground.

Enormous varactyl
(VA-RACK-TILL)
wander around
the rocky land.
They are good
climbers.

An Utai

The Utai ride the varactyl.

A varactyl

The red planet of Mustafar
(MUSS-TAH-FAR) is
a very hot place.
It is covered in fiery volcanoes.
Hot, melted rock called lava
flows from the volcanoes.
The sky is filled with black smoke
that blocks out the sun.

Fight on Mustafar

Two Jedi Knights, Obi-Wan Kenobi and Anakin Skywalker, fought each other on Mustafar. Anakin had turned from good to evil. Obi-Wan won the fight.

The space rock known as
Polis Massa (POE-LISS-MASS-AH)
has a medical center.
This is where space travelers can go
if they are sick.

The doctors are helped
by special robots
called droids.

Medical droid

Polis Massa doctors

Birth place

Padmé Amidala came to Polis Massa to give birth. She had twins.

The moon Yavin 4 is covered
in thick jungle.
The ruins of very old buildings
called temples rise above the trees.

At one time, the soldiers
who lived on Yavin 4 kept watch
for enemy starships from
the tops of the tallest temples.

What's inside the temples?

The temples were once used to keep starships. There were also rooms where people could eat and sleep.

The ice planet Hoth
is so cold that people can
freeze to death there.

On Hoth, people ride around on
large beasts called tauntauns.

Wampa ice creatures
live in ice caves.
They hang
the animals that
they catch from
the cave roof.

One time, a wampa even captured
a Jedi Knight!

The planet Dagobah (DAY-GO-BA) is covered in thick forests and swampy land.

The air is steamy, and it rains a lot.

There are many deadly creatures and poisonous plants.

The Jedi Master Yoda went
to hide on Dagobah.
He lived in a small tree house.

Crash landing

Young pilot
Luke Skywalker
crashed his
starship on
Dagobah.
Yoda found Luke
and took him to
his tiny house.

Cloud City floats in the skies of
the planet Bespin.

Visitors come to enjoy
its lively shops, restaurants,
and hotels.

A cloud car

Cloud cars fly around the city.

They have room for two passengers.

The forest moon of
the planet Endor is
the home of small, furry
creatures called Ewoks.
They live in the trees and
use simple tools and spears.

At night, Ewoks stay in the villages that they build high up in the trees.

We hope that you have enjoyed your trip to the *Star Wars* galaxy. Come back soon!

Fascinating facts

There are millions and millions of planets and suns in the enormous *Star Wars* galaxy.

Some of the skyscrapers on Coruscant are nearly a mile high.

The Queen of Naboo lives in the Royal Palace. This beautiful building has large windows and polished stone floors.

The trees on Kashyyyk are very tall. The Wookiees make houses in the trees.

The tauntauns have thick gray fur to protect them from the cold on Hoth.

STAR WARS®
A Queen's Diary

Written by Simon Beecroft

My name is Padmé Amidala.

I am the Queen of my planet.

Today I am going to start a diary.

I am going to start a diary because my life is very busy.

I do not want to forget anything.

My world

If people read this diary in the future, they might not know about my world. So I am going to explain interesting things about my world in these boxes.

Today I tried to count all the rooms in the palace, where I live.
I quickly lost count.
My palace is so large I think I shall never be able to explore all of it.

I love to climb up to one of the highest rooms.
Then I gaze at the waterfalls that flow down the side of the mountain.

Home world

I live on a planet called Naboo.
Naboo is a small planet.
It is very beautiful.

Today a lot of important people visited me.

When people meet me, some of them are surprised that I am so young.

I am just 14 years old.

All queens on my planet are young.

I am not even the youngest!

Even though I am not very old, I want to be a good queen.

Landspeeder

This morning I flew in a landspeeder.
I love travelling fast in landspeeders.
I flew around the city and looked at
all the pretty buildings.
Lots of people waved at me.

My palace is in the biggest city on Naboo, but I have not always lived here.

I was born in a mountain village.

People of Naboo

The humans who live on my planet are called the Naboo. I am one of them. The Naboo live in cities and villages.

I was learning about the Gungans
in my lessons today.

I learned that the Gungans also
live on my planet.

They live in underwater cities.

The Gungans can also live on land.

I would like to meet a Gungan.

Naboo natives

The Naboo and the Gungans do not often meet each other. They are not enemies, but they are not friends either!

Gungan   *Naboo*

I often think about my
parents and sisters.
I have many memories
of growing up
in my village.

When I was young,
my teachers realized
I was very clever.
My teachers gave me
extra training.
Later, people
decided to vote for
me as Queen.
It was the proudest
day of my life!

Padmé

Ruwee

Sola

Jobal

Eirtaé

Rabé

I have handmaidens who look
after me and help me dress.
They also protect me from danger.

My handmaidens are my friends, too.
Eirtaé (pronounced AIR-TAY)
and Rabé are two of my
closest handmaidens.

Royal dress
On my planet,
kings and queens
wear special clothes
and makeup.
They also wear their
hair in special ways.

Today I am going to visit a nearby planet in my special spaceship. My spaceship is totally silver.

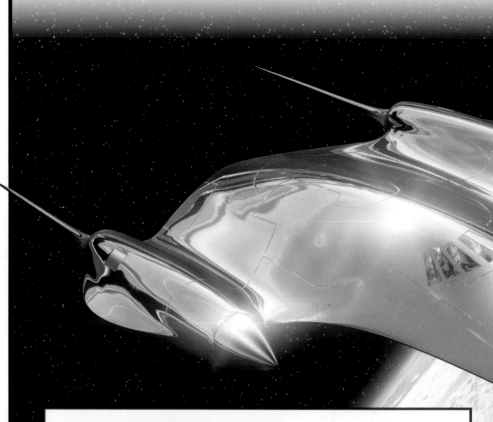

Spaceships

Naboo kings and queens fly silver spaceships. There is even a throne in my ship!

It has large rooms inside.

No one has a spaceship like mine.

I am even learning to fly it.

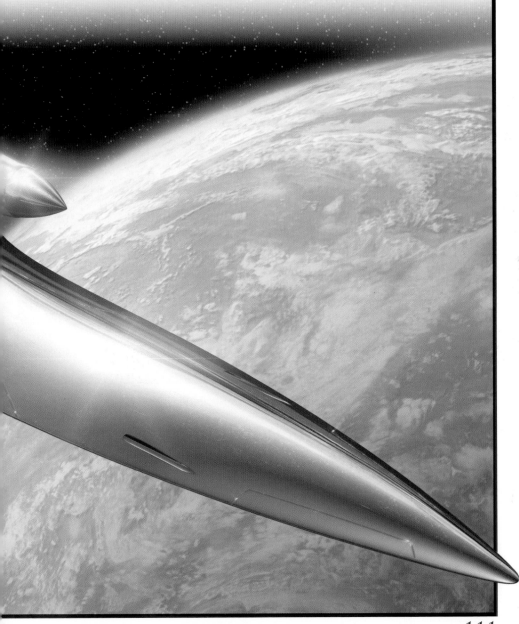

Sabé

Sometimes it is hard being Queen,
because everyone knows me.
Sabé is my best friend
and one of my handmaidens.

Padmé

Sometimes Sabé dresses as me,
and I dress as a handmaiden.
We have a secret way of talking
in code when we are in disguise.

A terrible thing has happened.
My planet has been invaded.
Enemy soldiers tried to capture me,
but I was saved by two Jedi Knights.
I had never met a Jedi before,
but I had heard about them.
They travel everywhere to help
people in need.

Droid soldiers

The enemy soldiers are machines called droids. Every droid soldier is armed and dangerous.

Now we are flying away from my planet to search for help for my people.

We have landed on a planet
to repair the spaceship.

The planet is rough and dry.

We went to a local town.

I went in disguise so no one
would know I was a queen.

I met a boy who is a slave.

This means that someone
owns him, and he is not free
to ever leave his master.

This young boy is very special.

His name is Anakin.

He told me I looked like an angel.

I think we will be friends.

The Jedi think that
Anakin is special.
They think that he
might have special
powers, like a Jedi.
They want to free
him from slavery,
so he can learn how
to be a Jedi.

Amazing news! Anakin is free! He won a dangerous race in his Podracer to gain his freedom. Now we can get help for my planet.

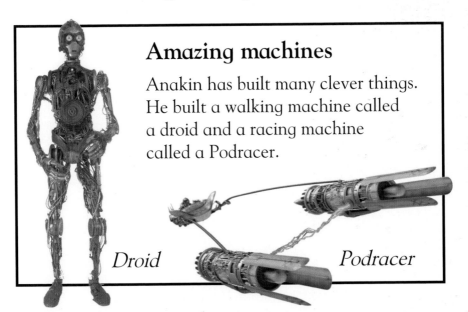

Amazing machines

Anakin has built many clever things. He built a walking machine called a droid and a racing machine called a Podracer.

Droid

Podracer

Today I became a fighter.
No one would help my people,
so I had to help them myself.
I went with the Jedi to ask the
Gungans for help.

Together we made an army
and fought the enemy droid soldiers.
The Gungans fought bravely,
but many of them died.

Weapons

The Gungans use
many weapons in
battle, including
giant catapults.

My planet is free!

Anakin helped us a lot.

He flew a spaceship straight into the

invaders' spaceship and blew it up!

Although it was really an accident,

when Anakin destroyed the ship the

droids could no longer fight.

Now I'm sure Anakin

will be trained as a Jedi.

Perhaps we will

meet again....

Places I have visited

I traveled to the swamps on my planet. The Gungans have a secret meeting place there.

I visited a dangerous planet called Tatooine with the Jedi Qui-Gon Jinn. We went to a busy town.

When I was visiting Tatooine, I watched a fast sporting race called a Podrace. A huge crowd gathered to watch the race.

I flew to the center of the galaxy to visit the capital planet. One enormous city covers the entire planet.

Index

Index